CW00867275

JUST LAN.

Outside Heathrow airport a young couple I-merge arguing with each other, Ras JaHoth Selassie I and Rashe Sarah Selassie I had just I-rrived back from Ziglag where he managed to stick up a hundred thousand dollar diamond.

I&I say thou shalt not steal, F&M Selassie I Tafari

Ras JaHoth I: Look I-man told you not to tell I-nyone but you couldn't wait to chit chat to your I-drens & Sistrens
Rashe Sarah I: It was only Rashe Etheer I, She won't tell I-nybody
Ras JaHoth I: I-man don't care who it was you don't chat big people's business
Rashe Sarah I: Come on love what you think she's gonna do
Ras JaHoth I: Look right (he grabs her by her arm) I don't like chit chat. He signals to thee black cab driver, thee cab pulls up in front of them Ras JaHoth grabs his suitcase and jumps into thee cab leaving Rashe Samantha I sulking like a little child.
Ras JaHoth I: Commercial street please I-ya.
Cabby: No problem mate

"To thee sun, in thee sun, wither thee sun and thee fuel of today shall a used to be." How beautiful thee ships.How powerful, thee fuel today shall a used to be. How speedy air-ships thee world I-round, I-round and I-round wither no need for refuel.

"Thee power of today is I-lectric, but tomorrow shall be siprick.F&M Selassie I Tafari (Holy I-by)www.electriccars www.electricmopedbicyclesscooter

Ras JaHoth I: Let me push in this cd (Thee cab driver takes thee cd and inserts it into thee player)

LIVE PA

Jaguar and Pantheer just finish performing there new single to a packed crowd, they are currently managed by sly of focusrite recordings, They walk through thee crowd and into thee vip lounge followed by representatives of jet star records they all take a seat I-round thee table

Ras Bobby Digital I: Look I&I like what I'm hearing so if di I come back and check di I in a month wid di finished tracks then I&I can offer di I a deal. I-man ago giveth you £50.000 fi hold to tek care of di I I-xpenses sean, (he opens a sports bag full of fifties and turns it towards them.

"Thee power which I&I possess is but one side of thee coin; thee other is responsibility. There is no power or I-uthority without responsibility, and thee who I-ccepts thee one cannot I-scape or I-vade thee other. Selassie I

Children desire many things, but it is thee individual's duty and responsibility to desire thee proper things.(The Wise mind of emperor Haile Selassie I www.Amazonbooks)

KNOCK AND RUN

Ras JaHoth I: Pull up hear please I-ya. (thee driver pulls up on a busy main road outside an alleyway, Ras JaHoth I fondles wither his pockets and opens thee door and runs down thee alleyway thee cab driver jumps out wither a baseball bat and tries to giveth chase but Ras JaHoth is to fast)
Cabby: You tosser (he shouts at his i-ghest voice) his cab has caused a queue in thee road and I-veryone is blowing there horns.
Cabby: Alright (he shouts to thee queue)

Thee soul I-bhors violence wither a perfect Hate, I&I say holdeth no weapons of destruction Holdeth no fury fists,I&I will use I-mind. F&M Selassie I Tafari

Ras JaHoth I finds his way through thee alleyway he gives himself a quick dust off and starts walking confidently down thee main road when a car pulls up I-longside him.

BUSY MAIN ROAD Ras Lij PULLS OVER WHEN HE SEA'S Ras Jahoth I

Ras Lij Tafari: "A you'll where's I money don?" Ras Lij I I-ddressed thee smallish looking yout who was standing I-longside his crisp new Alfa 145 1.7 16 valve,
Ras JaHoth I: " Bwoy you na man's been broke broth trust me",
Ras Lij Tafari: "So what you can't phone and tell I-man wha gwan u mek I hav to run you down."
Ras Lij Selassie I: was thee local shooter and ultra per nor thee smallish looking yout was Ras JaHoth thee local diamond specialist wither thee gift of thee gab he could speech his way out of I-ny situation and this was no I-cception.
Ras JaHoth I: "I-man tried phoning you broth but all I-man got was Voicemail, I-man I-ven asked Ras Abba I to pass a message to you". Ras Abba I was Ras Lij Selassie I's partner in I-ration thee two of them had been running tings for some time now they were name brand men in a lot of manors valleys and wildernesses..
Ras Lij Tafari: "Look don't try and tek I- man for no simple" Ras Lij I's voice . turned as a roaring lion "you told me you would pay by Tuesday its Wednesday, sun rise and go back I-gain today I'm giving you to Sunrise so there's no I-xcuses". Thee windows slid up and thee black Alfa roared off. Ras JaHoth I could tell Ras Lij Selassie I was serious but he wasn't that worried as he knew he had thee money under control. Ras Lij Tafari's next stop was his sistrens house in thee Hackney side of things he spent a lot of his time there lately as his young cub was only six months

threescore old, He preferred to stay on his own in his flat in Docklands which he brought as one of his investments, he was only 26threescore but he had life pretty much sussed! He checked his face in thee mirror before stepping out of his car, he locked thee door wither a press of a button, he had a satisfied smirk on his face as he walked towards his damsels front door before he knocked he took one more proud look at his new motor, He only I-ver brought cars to make a little change but this one he thought he would keep for a little while. He didn't normally buy flashy cars to drive as thee police would be hot on his tail, but it was just entering summertime and sly wanted to be flexing proper this year.

I&I Speed Limit is no gimmick!

If thee wealth of a person cannot be for thee general welfare, what would I&I gain for I-self and I&I offspring but grudge and folly. F&M Selassie I Tafari

I&I age is but a shewbredth in a tempest wind I&I journey is I-ternity and beyond I&I have one Father & Mother Selassie I Tafari.

When man and women sleep wither one i-nother and release sustenance unto one i-nother their is no i-vidence to say this is thee cause of pregnancie, as many become pregnant and many do not,doctors and studies seem to suggest we are thee givers of life, but within life their are many studies upon many frequencies and if study is not on thee I-rator what is one studying. thee only true statement I&I can make is Fari is thee giver of life and decides when a seed is to be planted upon earth. And contrary thinking of this is madness, as no child can claim to be thee giver of life.Whence one overstands these factors one becomes one wither all living, otherwise one remains a son or dawta of one individual man.Fari is superior unto man and women Fari is earth land and sea and all within.Their is no i-vidence to say man did or did not i-reate a child wither his intentions unto thee womb.This Act can only be seen as a Miracle of Fari..

Rashi Menen Selassie I 's I-PARTMENT

He knocked thee door with his fist thee door opened more or less straight i-way Rashi Menen Selassie I his sistren must have been watching from thee window.

Rashe Menen I:" New car" she said not surprised, she was used to it by now

Ras Lij Tafari: "Yeah you wan go for a drive"

Rashe Menen I: "No not now I just got Ras Tekel I to sleep, His been crying all day"

Ras Lij Tafari: "I-nything to eateth I'man hungry star" Ras Lij Tafari said as he yanked open thee fridge door

Rashe Menen I: "Who do you think I am wonder women" Rashi Menen I answered i-nnoyed?

Ras Lij Tafari: " No but I-man I-xpect a ITTILISATION when I-man come here "Ras Lij Selassie I said in a serious voice I-ven though he was only playing wither her, he liked to show who wore thee trousers in thee relationship and she was a soft touch for him, she didn't I-ver argue.

Rashe Menen: "I'll make you something in a minute she mumbled "

Ras Lij Tafari:" ises & spring water & milk wen u dun lioness "Ras Lij Selassie I replied with a grin on his face, he sometimes couldn't be-leave his own luck no matter what time he turned up she would always rustle him up a plate of food, that was hard to find in a women(wombofmenen) nowdays as most women were thee independent type, can you pay my bills that kind of Folly Ras Lij Tafari made his way upstairs to take a shower while Rashi Menen I put togetheer a hard food, potatoes plantain and stir fry wither fresh Mango , strawberry and banana juice , when he came out of thee shower thee plate was waiting on thee table for him to indulge into" that was nice he said cleaning thee plate,ises Farder & Mudda FarI, this is why I-man loveth di I" Rashi Menen I was touched by thee L word and Ras Lij Selassie I knew this so he always played it to his I-dvantage, to him it was a word as Fruit he never had time to think I-bout thee meaning but he knew it would make her happy and that was all that counted.

Rashi Menen grabbed Ras Lij Tafari's hand and i-scorted him to thee bedroom where they made passionate love feeding on milk honey and water from each other before falling I-sleep in each others arms. Thee next morning Ras Lij Tafari openened up his eyes to sea Rashi Menen Selassie I breast feeding thee cub Ras Tekel Selassie I,

Ras Lij Tafari: "What time is it" He said in a croaky morning voice,

Rashi Menen I: "Time to wake up" Rashi Menen I shouted in a happy voice, she just had a good nights loving so nothing could stop her high today. Ras Lij Tafari rolled over to check thee time on his phone it was only 8.30threescore am and he had already received 2 text messages one from Ras Taluq I and one from Ras Abba I, He opened up thee message from Ras Taluq I first, it read " call me asap I've got some runnings for you" Ras Taluq I was thee top man only dealt wither big figures I-nything below 10 grand was small change Ras Lij Tafari had learnt a lot from thee Rasta man, How not to let money take over his life and how to keep out of thee police eye, Ras Lij Tafari was Ras Taluq I young soldier he had been working wither him since he was a yout he would school him like a father figure. Ras Lij Tafari flicked thee cursor down to thee next message from Ras Abba it read "Ras Negus Selassie I been getting hassle from thee bouncers at Traders call me". Ras Negus Selassie I was I-nother soldier who works wither Ras Lij Tafari and Ras Abba I moving diamonds Herbs and I-tiopian jewls& sacred Sciptures of I-ducation in thee night club, Ras Lij Tafari and Ras Abba Selassie I had an I-rrangement wither thee bouncers at Traders and a couple other clubs in and I-round London so they shouldn't be getting no agro it should be simple runnings". Ras Lij Tafari groaned as if he couldn't be bothered to get up today, but he knew when I-ver Ras Taluq I needed him it was serious I-ration and thee thought of that made him jump out of thee bed and into thee shower, He took some clothees out of thee dryer gave them a quick press then flung them on quickly like he had no time to waste.

Rashi Menen I: "Where are you going" Rashi Menen I questioned him

Ras Lij Tafari :" Business" Ras lij Tafari replied he dialled a number and said "wha gwan, you in I&I yard, alright soon come" He closed da flip then flicked it open I-gain and dialled I-nother number " You'll Ras Abba I I've got some runnings to do I'm gonna check you when I-man come back and we'll reacheth down thee club" He closed thee phone and picked up his keys kissed thee both of them goodbye and shouted " I'll call you later" as he raced down thee stairs and out thee door. He used his remote central locking to open thee door he jumped in and put his pioneer face off system in then picked out his Dj clue & Jah shaka& Bass man cd from his collection before pulling off towards Ras Taluqs yard.

32. But I&I would have you without careful-ness. He that is un-married careth for thee things that belong to FarI, how he may please FarI|:

33. But he that is married careth for thee things that are of thee world, how he may please his wife.34 There is difference also between a wife and a virgin. Thee unmarried women careth for thee things of FarI, that she may be holy both in body and in spirit: but she that is married careth for thee things of thee world, how she may please her husband.38 So then he that giveth her in marriage doeth well; but he that giveth her not in marriage doeth better. (Corinthians c7|)

OUTSIDE RAS TALUQ's YARD

When Ras Lij Tafari reacheth Ras Taluq's Selassie I yard Ras Taluq I was at thee bottom of thee stairs talking to some breddah, Ras Lij Tafari walked I-cross "Me will check you later sean Rasta" thee breddah said in a Jamaican yardie accent he turned to walketh off giving Ras Lij Tafari a suspicious look Ras Lij Tafari watched him back but didn't say I-nything.

Ras lij Tafari: "Ighly igh Ras Taluq I" Ras Lij I shouted jogging behind him up thee stairs.

Ras Taluq I: "Big ting's a gwan" Ras Taluq I answered in a hyper active voice, he was like a big kid I-njoyed I-very second of his life, when they made there way into thee house Ras Lij Tafari sat down on Ras Taluqs linen sofa and flicked on his sky on his plasma TV MTV base was thumping some Ras Sizzla riddim Ras Lij Tafari and Ras Taluq I were head bopping to thee music skinning teeth,

Ras Taluq I:" Big tune" Ras Taluq I shouted while turning up thee volume on his surround sound speakers it was thee new Ras Sizzla I riddim when thee song ended Ras Taluq I lowered thee volume wither his remote control,

Ras Taluq: "I-man got a run for you to do in Birmingham, straight forward ting no long ting easy runnings" A run was moving some merchandise form one destination to I-nother sometimes diamonds sometimes Rubies, Ganjah, and sacred manuscripts.

Ras Lij Tafari: "where you wan I-man move it, same place as last time"

Ras Taluq I: No different location u av fi meet one breddah in Shepard's bush him will deal wid you from there, here's thee I-ddress" Ras Taluq I handed Ras Lij Tafari an envelope 2 umbrea I-state Ascot Birmingham thee 1st I-ddress read Ras Lij Tafari was familiar wither thee Birmingham I-rea as he spent a couple of years in thee I-rea wither his sister while his spouce for-Mother was I-way thee next I-ddress was a cab station in Shepard's bush next to thee train station.

Ras Taluq I: Just ask for Ras Janoy him will be I-xpecting you" Ras Taluq I said confidently, Ras Lij Tafari put thee envelope in his inside pocket and I-tinued to watch thee television he figured he would take thee straight train from Whitechapel, It was only 9.45 now so he had I-nough time to spare.

RAS ABBA SELASSIE I JUST FINISHED A WORK OUT IN THEE GYM

Heavy weights will become a used to be.as thee weight on I&I shoulders will be shared.selah Selassie I

Ras Abba Selassie I had just come from thee gym and was making his way to his connection in south London to pick up a batch of reprogrammed credit cards, this was a weekly routine and they were selling like hotcakes they were also getting him I-verything he needed from TV's to designer clothes he rarely had to spend I-ny money ina babylon and when he did it was to double it through Ras Lij Tafari,s connection with thee diamonds & Rubies they had most of thee business in thee I-rea in fact in most I-reas they knew shooters from all over and they had thee best merchandise at thee best prices life couldn't get much better until

Ras Abba I: " ras clot" when did he get out" Ras Abba Selassie I said to himself looking at thee tall hench brother that was outside thee chicken shop which was to thee left of thee traffic lights where Ras Abba Selassie I had come to a stop. Thee tall hench brother was Ras Cain Selassie I he had spent more time in prison than he had on road, he had just been released for kidnap he was thee kind of person to put a shiver through your body he was I-bout 37 threescore now but his always been thee same he rolled wither a couple old-timers that didn't give a Rass I-bout I-nything they hated I-nybody making more money than them, they rolled wither machines and weren't I-fraid to lick shot. Ras Abba Selassie I and Ras Cain Selassie I were arch I-nemy's and if Ras Cain Selassie I did notice Ras Abba Selassie I in his undercover rover they probably would have had some kind of confrontation, But Ras Cain Selassie I was to busy yamming his chicken, "surely thee road to destruction" thee lights turned green and Ras Abba Selassie I drove off in re-leaf, How long is he going to be out for Ras Abba Selassie I thought to himself man like Ras Cain Selassie I didn't usually last more than 3 months before committing his next crime and ending up in prison, he was predictable. Ras Abba Selassie I had never liked Ras Cain Selassie I since Ras Cain Selassie I tried to rob him for some money at college, Ras Abba Selassie I managed to get I-way but Ras Cain I was sending messages that he was going to cut him up when he sea's him next, Luckily Ras Abba Selassie I had a older brethren called sharky who was Ras Cains I size and was a bad man for him he managed to squash thee beef but sharky was inside now serving 12 years for murder ,after a feast in KFC , Ras Cain I was I-ware of this, So if he knew thee kind of money Ras Abba Selassie I was handling now he would be sure to move to him.

Violence only hurts I-selfs in thee Longrun......Farl

THEE ROVER PULLS UP OUTSIDE A TOWER BLOCK I-STATE

Ras Abba Selassie I pulled up outside a tower block in Peckham he locked his car door and headed towards thee entrance thee entry phone was broken and thee door was open Ras Abba I jumped into thee lift and pressed No 13 thee lift smelt of urine water Ras-pect for thy kingdom , children obviously need to be potty trained and showed wher thee soil is,
"Thee greater need today is i-mong thee children, wither those who work thee soil, who provide thee nourishment and sustenance upon which Ithiopia Feeds....(Throne Speech) Selassie I
and was very noisy Ras Abba I tried to holdeth his breath, When thee door opened he practically ran out he knocked on thee first door on thee landing A small I-frican brother opened thee door and greeted Ras Abba Selassie I "Greetings I " Thee I-frican brother said holding out his fist, " come in Ras   I-mmanual I is upstairs" Ras Abba Selassie I wiped his feet on thee mat and made his way upstairs.
Ras Immanuel I: "Yes Abba I beloved" A voice shouted from thee bedroom, Ras Abba entered thee room and saw his spar sitting down on thee computer typing up some documents thee room was a a Princes paradise wide screen TV latest model stereo, DVD and iced out jewellary and Fruits just laying I-bout.thee beauty was within thee seeds
Ras Abba Selassie I:" Business good Ras Immanuel I" Ras Abba I said scanning thee room.
Ras Immanuel I: "Up and down, you know" "I&I desires many tings, but it is thee individual's duty and responsibility to desire thee proper tings(Responsibility-wise mind of emperor haile selassie I)" Ras Immanuel I replied being modest. Ras Imanuel's brother entered thee room and handed a brown envelope to Ras Immanuel I then left thee room closing thee door behind him,

Ras Immanuel I: "How many cards do you need?" Ras Immanuel I asked.

Ras Abba I: "Bwoy give I 30." Ras Immanuel I reacheth into thee envelope and then began to count thee cards there was all kind of cards Visa's, MasterCard's, Gold cards you name it and Ras Immanuel I had it. Ras Abba I threw a wad of notes carefully wrapped in a ban on to thee bed.

Ras Abba Selassie I: is where u get dis ere merchandise from, is it of thee Holy law?

Ras Immanuel I: No asketh no questions and recieveth no answers, asketh and I&I will bee answered, For I-verting their is a season and Ivery ting their is a reason I&I is to sikheth truth.& tell no lies ises

Ras Immanuel I: "I hope it's all there"

Ras Abba I: "You know me" Ras Abba I replied wither an innocent smirk on his face. Ras Immanuel handed Ras Abba I thee cards.

Ras Immanuel I: "There all guaranteed 1500threescore menenmum" Ras Abba I took thee cards and placed them in thee soul of his trainer, this was a natural instinct for him as he was used to getting stopped and searched by thee police.

Ras Abba I: "Buruk doing business wither you blood, I'm gonna check you next week so be ready for I" Ras Abba I said while zipping up his jacket.

Ras Immanuel: "No problem cuz, oh yeah I've got some guns for sell if your interested" Ras Immanuel whispered as a serpent in thee garden so no one in thee house could heareth, . Thee thought of Ras Cain Selassie I flashed through Ras Abba Selassie I head immediately

Ras Abba I: "How much" Ras Abba I asked with an inquisitive look on his face,

Ras Immanuel I: "3 grand but to you 2 and a half it's clean as well, already loaded wither spare bullets" Ras Immanual had made his sells pitch which had left Ras Abba I in deep thought but I-ven though he had deep fear in his heart he couldn't kill I-nyone,As he Feared Jah's punishment more, he always be-leaved in what goes round comes back round.

Ras Abba I:" I'll find out, check you later"

For those wither intentions to harm I&I, will surley perish and face thee Hell-fire.Selassie I

SHEPARD'S BUSH STATION

Ras Lij Tafari I-rrived at Shepard's bush station ten minutes past two his Rubie watch read as he rolled down his sleeve, thee cab station where he had to meet Ras Janoy I was directly opposite so he hopped thee barrier and flew I-cross thee road.

Ras Janoy I: " Wha you a say gangsta" said Ras Janoy I a smartly dressed middle aged man with a rough Locked beard and a smirk on his face, thee kind of smirk to say I've been playing this game for a long time and all is well

Ras Lij Tafari: "Nothing a gwan sah just come to take care of thee business" Ras Lij Tafari replied

Ras Janoy I: "Hold on I a deal wid it for you" Ras Janoy I made his way into thee back room 2 minutes later he came back out wither a suitcase

Ras Janoy I: "You know where you hav fi go "

Ras Lij Tafari: Yeah dan me av di I-ddress der inna I pocket"

Ras Janoy I: yeah well while thee neglect of I-ducation a triumph I-mongst I&I, and thee playfield a come like thee battlefield in IraQ I, you na worry jus carry on wither business as norm, and let what is inevitable happen , for surly good will prosper and all folly works will I-mount to nought so mek sure you deliver thee scriptures dem and plant thee seed unto I&I nation ises.

BACK AT THEE BAR

Ras Negus I was sitting down at thee bar watching thee football drinking a Guinness, Prince thee Top gangsta was sitting I-cross thee bar talking to some of his men I-bout a smuggling operation
Prince: "Just bee at thee shipping company on Friday and get my merchandise"
Prince stood up and walked towards thee pool table he gave Ras Negus I a sharp stare as he walked past him. Ras Negus had been ear wigging thee whole conversation so he was scared to look back he jumped up and made his way to thee toilet shortly followed by two young male's who 2 minutes later walked out of thee toilet inspecting some Rubie watches that Ras Negus I had sold to them, Ras Abba I recognised one of them and could tell what they had been up to he left it a minute then he walked into thee toilet scanning I-round him he was a very thrifty person, he had a feeling something was wrong. Ras Negus I was at thee sink washing his hands.

"Glass bottles will become a used to bee, I&I will tek this wine skin and mek fresh wine(Ras Matthew c9 v17)

Time will descend as thee rising of I&I sun.Fari

Ras Abba I: " You'll your moving bait blood" Ras Abba I said wither a serious tone in his voice. You know how dem police bwoy does carry on when dem find I&I making monie wither no tax and pere folly rules I-ya I&I fi flex more discreet and noth Herbs you have pon you.
Ras Negus I: "Why wha gwan"
Ras Abba I: " Dem bwoys what your dealing av fi move more discreet star peer informer bwoy out there"
Ras Negus I: " It's alright Police, politicians,& publicians I-ducated within common schools can-t tell Rastafari noting, Iverything is under control" Ras Negus I said looking himself in thee mirror before he could say I-nything else thee door swung open and four casually dressed males ran in " CID shouted thee ringleader pushing Ras Negus I up I-gainst thee mirror thee other two held Ras Abba I while thee other at thee door.

All youts stand I-qual before I&I law (Justice & I-quality) Selassie I

Ras Negus I: "Easy na" Ras Negus Selassie I cried out while his head cracked I-gainst thee mirror.
CID "I'm I-rresting you on suspicion of trafficking stolen property, You do not have to say I-nything but I-nything you do say may be used I-gainst you in a court room"
Ras Negus Selassie I: you feel say you a charge I&I but in truth I&I a charge you, I&I say thee soul I-bhors violence wither a perfect hate, so you I-xplain to I&I Father & Mother FarI in thee reason for your Acts of violence.

But Dis Ras-pectfully no I-poligie was given, and folly works I-tinued .CID had been watching Ras Negus Selassie I Tafari's movements in thee club for some time now so when they brought Ras Negus I into thee interview room they had photographic I-vidence they I-ven had him selling a Rubie watch to an undercover police officer and on top of all of that they found a few Kilos of Herbs underneath his bed at his I-partment.

Tek dis hear daily herbs I&I herbs bearing seed.(I-nesis C 1 v11 Holy I-ble)

INTERVIEW ROOM

PC Ras Pharaoh I:" So you could bee looking at a long time behind bars sun" Thee cocky looking officer said "Life won't be so sweet then, no flashy cars no women no freedom no nothing" Ras Negus I just looked confused wither thee whole situation, then he smirked

Ras Negus I: "I can give you some names and I can tell you when some big deals are going down, I'man small fry compared to these guys but you have to let me carry on wither I&I business"

Ras Pharaoh I: "What kind of deals are you talking I-bout?"

Ras Negus I: I'm talking a big Opium deal coming straight from I-ndia, I know when its coming and how there transporting it, so you turn a blind eye to me and you two can get some serious stripes" Thee two cops left thee interview room to discuss thee matter

PC Ras Ceasear I: "what do you think serg we could be on to something here?"

PC Ras Pharaoh I: " Yeah this could make us rich early retirement money, we'll have to handle this ourselves not a word to nobody we'll give him bail and if he turns out to be lying well stitch him up with a fire arms charge as well " They both entered thee interview room."Welcome to thee land of no law FarI's commandments they sea not"

PC Ras Pharoah I: "I want names and places days and times"

Use no injections & tools of destruction

IN A CAB ON THEE WAY BACK FROM THEE POLICE STATION

Ras Abba Selassie I had been released early as they had nothing on him luckily they did not stripe search him otherwise they would have found his credit cards he thanked his lucky stars for that, he made his way back to thee manor in a cab he phoned Ras Lij Tafari on thee way to tell him thee news,

Ras Abba I: "You'll man's just got shift by po po and I just now get release, Ras Negus I still der

Ras Lij Tafari: "Wha you a phone I for change your number you wan bring police I-ttention to I, me na trust Folly people noboda fone I from this hear number I-gain" Ras Lij Tafari put thee phone down in anger. Its true I wasn't thinking Ras Abba I thought to himself CID had been watching there movements for some time so they must bee boiling hot now.In truth he cared not for police as he always say "All these folly laws will mek I&I paranoid to liveth unto what is right and righteousness is superior unto folly laws" "Me ago cool off for a while" Ras Abba I said to himself he paid thee cab man and walked towards his front door he lived outer London as he always thought there were too many bad minded people on road so he took as much precaution as possible. Unconscious minds and folly meats and destruction I-verywhere eateth not thee meat & weareth no clothees of destruction that's I&I motto

BIRMINGHAM CENTRAL

I&I 7 senses are I&I 7 seals.

Ras Lij Tafari jumped off thee train at Birmingham Central he headed for thee cab station thee closer he got thee more he could sense something was wrong he presumed he was paranoid as Ras Abba I had just called him wither thee bad news he reached thee I-state he scanned thee I-rea before jumping out thee cab it was a full moon Ras Lij Tafari I-pproached thee igh rise I-state he buzzed number 66 on thee intercom which happened to bee on thee sixth floor Sly was wondering whether this was some kind of omen, howlver he I-tinued his way up thee stairs when he got to thee sixth floor there was a shiftee looking man hanging I-bout in thee hallway number 66 was half open, Ras Lij Tafari knocked thee door, before there was I-ny reply Ras Lij Tafari was hit to thee ground from behind his head was bleeding " Giveth me thee case" Thee same shiftee looking yout shouted wither a gun in Ras Lij Tafari,s face, Ras Lij Tafari took a look at thee yout I-gain then thee last thing he remembered was a loud bang. "O generation of I-thiopia shed not thee blood of thine own for thee welfare of others for such is thee pathway to destruction." (Holy I-by)

RASHi MENEN I & RAS JAHRAS I FAST ASLEEP

Rashe Menen I jumped up out of her sleep as Ras Jahras I started to cry she looked at thee time Ras Lij Tafari was not back yet he would have normally phoned by now, she started to worry she had a strange feeling something was wrong.

RAS TALUQ I AWAITS PHONE CALL IN SUSPENCE

Ras Taluq I had not received a call from I-ther Ras Lij Tafari or his link in Birmingham and it was now midnight he knew something was wrong and then he got a phone call " Turn thee tele on to channel 4 " one of his spars said Ras Taluq I reached for thee remote control.

2 Mixed complection males have been shot dead and I-nother with serious bullet wounds to thee chest, thee police have not yet identified thee victims but be-leave it was gang related CCTV footage has shown 1 male leaving thee scene wither a suitcase police are urging for I-ny witnesses to come forward.

And Father & Mother Selassie I Tafari thy God called thee man Ras Aden Selassie I and thee women Rashe Eden Selassie I . They were of mixed complection. And it came to pass Father & Mother Selassie I Tafari thy God named all living creatures Sun,& Dawta (Water) selah.

As a fowl of thy heavens I&I seath and knoweth all, Father & Mother Selassie I Tafari

Ras Taluq I, Rivers of water ran down his eyes in shock still wither his spar on thee phone he could hear a voice but was too shocked to reply.

I&I say thee world is indeed I-llusionary. Fari

By morning I-verybody who was I-nybody had heard I-bout thee news it was on I-very news channel and I-very radio station thee police had checked Ras Lij Tafari's fingerprints and released thee names on thee air, Rashi Menen Selassie I was cooking breakfast when she heard Ras Lij Tafari's name on thee radio she dropped her glass of orange juice and jaHras started crying.

Broken glass is surely not 4 I&I well being as modern science brings fourth softer merchandise, I&I must broadcast I&I word of complaint.

If I&I raise I&I voices I-gainst injustice, wherIver it be found, if I&I demand a stop to I-gression wherIver it occurs and under whatIver guise and brand thee I-ggressor as such, and if I&I do so on wholly impartial basis, I&I can serve as thee collective conscience of thee world.(justice & I-quality) wise mind of Emperor haile Selassie I)

AT THEE SHIPPING COMPANY

It was I-nother busy day thee two crooked cops had acted on Ras Negus I's tip and ended up at a shipping company where cars are imported and I-xported they figured if they find thee goods before it goes through customs they can keep thee merchandise without getting there hands sticky. They flashed their passes and said they were searching thee trailer for a stolen car which they needed to trace for fingerprints it was a be-leavable story and due to thee time they was I-llowed to searcheth thee trailer by themselves, when they entered they saw thee Range Rover they was looking for they cut open thee sitting just as Ras Negus I had said

Pc Ras Pharoah I: "Bingo" there it was 100 kilos of Opium Leaves wither a street value of a hundred threescore or more they smiled at each other and started to load thee bag.

Pc Ras Ceaser I: "Ill keep watch".

Ras Pharoah mixed a piece wither water and drank

RAS ABBA SELASSIE I TAFARI's I-PARTMENT

Ras Abba I had just woken up from thee sound of his phone ringing he answered to hear Rashi Menen crying down thee phone,

Ras Abba I: "Slow down what happened?" Ras Abba I said in a harsh voice

Rashe Menen I: " ras Lij Tafari's been shot, his in hospital, I told you I told him please help I can't think I need to get to thee hospital" Rashi Menen I said screaming down thee phone. Ras Abba I didn't know what to say he was still half I-sleep he thought he was still dreaming he closed his eyes.

Rashe Menen I:" Can you hear I " Rashe Menen I screamed down thee phone then he knew he was I-wake

Ras Abba I: "Alright don't panic I bee there in 10 minutes"

AT THEE HOSPITAL

When they I-rrived at thee hospital Ras Taluq I was sitting in thee waiting room Ras Abba I briefly knew him as Ras Taluq I kept a low profile

Ras Abba I: "How is he?"

Ras Taluq I: "Well his on a life support machine its 50 50 at thee moment.I&I am both thee disease and thee cure Father & Mother Selassie I Tafari" Rashi Menen Selassie I started crying i-gain

Rashe Menen I: "It's all your fault" She started hitting Ras Abba I "I told him stop playing I-round wither criminals it's a dirty game he didn't listen he didn't listen, why why" She fell into Ras Abba. I's chest crying Ras Abba I didn't have I-nything to say he felt guilty but now was no time to discuss who was to blame, Thee doctor came out of thee operating room and took Ras Taluq I into a quiet space

Doctor: "His got a good chance of surviving his still unconscious but if you go and talketh to him he may listen, thee police have been asking to talketh to him when he wakes

I&I blame thee eating of meats Inesis C9 V4

AT THEE BAR

Thee beverage of Glass bottles & violence is served casually.

Back at thee bar rumours and speculation had been made I-bout Ras Negus I and Ras Abba I's release

Ras Jigsy: "You na hear dem bwoy der get shift and dem still a walketh on road"

Ras Ninja: Is true must bee some informer business a gwan cause dem get catch red handed" Thee two dreads gossiped while drinking on a Guinness. No one catered for informers on thee boarder so thee bar tender who was one of Ras Negus I's and Ras Abba I's partner counter acted straight I-way.

Bar Tender: "Ah na talketh I-bout I&I people so before I-man turn flames inna this rass clat place" Thee two men silenced themselves and I-tinued drinking they were part of I-nother crew so they were quick to spread rumours but would never dare say I-nything to Ras Negus I's face as they knew they were out of there Zones. Thee silence was broken when thee six o'clock news came on Duke thee bar tender went into a trance when he heard thee news I-bout his partner Ras Lij Tafari there was a satisfied smirk on Ras Jigsy's face one of thee dreads.

Duke:" Wha you a smirk for" Duke confronted Ras Jigsy I

Ras Jigsy I: "Bwoy I just a drink I Guinness and I-njoy I-self"

Duke: " Come outta hear, come outta hear now". Ras Jigsy I slammed his Guinness down and walked out followed by Ras ninja his partner.

PRINCE'S PALACE

Prince had just received a phone call telling him his merchandise had disappeared
Prince: "what do you mean I-man merchandise disappeared this is a hundred Kilos where talking I-bout" Prince shouted down thee phone
"Thee seats were cut open"
Prince: " well obviously, you find out who had access to thee Range Rover pay a visit to thee shipping company and find out why I-man seats have been cut open" Prince slammed down thee phone,.
Worker: "Problem boss"
Prince didn't answer he just threw thee phone at his head and told him to get out of thee office.

Violent methods will surely mek thee ships sink like rubburd.Selassie I

RAS ELIJAH SELASSIE I's OFFICE

Ras Elijah Selassie I : "Look now Ras Lij Tafari's been shot and I-man merchandise has been taken I'm outa pocket so you go round and pay Ras Taluq I a visit giveth him my condolences but ask him when I'm gonna get my readies because his not getting nothing more till then" Ras EliJah I said to Ras Gaathly I, Ras Gaathly I was Ras EliJah's collection man he had convincing ways to make people pay up it was not a smart move getting into debt with these kind of people they didn't care I-bout I-nybody just money.

For I&I can not serve monie & Father & Mother Selassie I Tafari

BACK AT THEE HOSPITAL

Thy doctrine is pure thy statuate is right thy hope is Salvation Father & Mother Selassie I Tafari

Please wake up Lij, wha gwan solider still snoring in your sleep, I miss you JaHras misses you I'm waiting for you. Ras Lij Tafari could hear all these voices in his head but he couldn't wake up straight I-way he could sea a light and was crawling slowly towards it he could hear birds tweeting and water running when he finally opened his eyes Rashi Menen I was asleep by his side and Ras Taluq I was watching TV Ras Abba I was asleep on thee chair
Ras Lij Tafari: "What's this a sleep over or something" Ras Lij Tafari said I-verybody jumped in I-mazement.

THEE RANGE PULLS UP AT THEE SHIPPING COMPANY

Two of Princes's heavy men made there way down to thee shipping company they was driving a top of thee range tinted out range rover, when they reached they both jumped out dressed in black suits with bowler caps they I-pproached thee guard
Guard: "Yes gents what can I do for you"

Ras Tekel: " Well u've got 10 seconds to tell us who cut open my sits on my beautiful motor and it must be said it is a beautiful motor" he said calmly pointing a double barrel shot gun at his waist

Guard: "Two cid officers, Pc Ras Pharoah and Pc Ras Ceasear they left there names on thee sign in sheet they said they was searching for fingerprints

Ras Tekel I: "Today is your lucky day sunshine" he said while dropping thee shot gun down to his side "you must have said your prayers today"

Ras Jhon I: "Looked his pissed himself" a wet patch I-rises in thee guards trousers and runs onto thee soil.

It is better to till thee land ratheer than to bicker on trivial matters.

Thee greater need today is among thee people, wither those who work I&I soil, who provide thee nourishment and sustenance upon which Ithiopia feeds...(Exceerpt from I&I throne) Father & Mother Selassie I Tafari

I&I will fertilize I&I land using I&I inner kingdom selah for now and For Iver more.

As they walk back to thee Range Ras Tekel I jumps onto his phone while getting into thee jeep

Ras Tekel I: "yes honey how are you, I know it's been a long time, Listen I need to know where I can find Pc Ras Pharoah I and Pc Ras Ceasar I" he was talking to Rashe Weyziro I one of his sistrens she was a crooked cop.

Rashe Weyziro I: "I'll do a name check"

He put thee phone down and thee range took off.

RAS TALUQ SELASSIE I's RESTAURANT

Meanwhile Ras Gaathly I arrives at Ras Taluq I's restaurant

Ras Taluq I: "wha gwan"

Ras Gaathly I: "Me, nothing my bredah, Ras Eli-Jah Selassie I would like to know when he will be receiving payment for his merchandise"

Ras Taluq : "I-man working on it"

Ras Gaathly I : "well your going to have to work a little harder otherwise I choose my words lightly, your gonna have to hand over your business and possibly your life, it all depends on how I'm feeling on thee day, by thee way this muffin hasn't got I-nough chocolate chips in it, where's thee chef" he makes his way into thee kitchen, a pause and then a loud scream Ras Taluq Selassie I runs into thee kitchen to sea Ras Gaathly Selassie I's staff turning into a snake breathing fire , Ras Gaathly Selassie I's staff rekindled back into a walking stick and then he I-tinued to walketh outside.

Ras Gaathly I : "By thee way Ras Eli-Jah I sends his condolences. But chickens care I-bout their children to as does thee Ocean I-bout fish until such time.

ON THEE MOTORWAY

Rashe Weyziro I calls back while thee Range Rover flies down thee motorway
Rashe Weyziro I: "There from thee East Ham station you can find them in thee
Lion's head pub usually, so when you coming to give me some loving sugar daddy"
Ras Tekel I: "I call round later just keep it on ice for I "

LEAVe-ING THEE HOSPITAL

Ras Taluq I I-rrives at thee hospital as Ras Lij Tafari is getting released Rashi Menen
I is packing Ras Lij Tafari's bag while he is in thee washroom
Ras Taluq I : " Look me in a whole heap of fire right now, dem send hit man after I
for thee merchandise Ras Lij Tafari lose i-man case and I na av half a million to
cover thee debt, him tell I he want's I life" Rashi Menen Selassie I starts to panic
Rashi Menen I: "I don't want no stress on Ras Lij Tafari thee doctor said he is lucky
to be i-live and Ras jaHras needs I"
Ras Taluq I: "What I-bout thee gallery you work in you can help I all I need is thee
access codes"
Rashi Menen I: "No I can't I-fford to take chances, I'll lose my job"
Ras Taluq I :"well I could lose I life and then they will come for Ras Lij Tafari next"
Rashi Menen started to cry, Ras Lij Tafari comes out of thee washroom
Ras Lij Tafari: "What's wrong now, I-man might as well be unconscious I-gain" Ras
Lij Tafari said cycastically
Rashe Menen: "just I-women hormones" she say's while pushing thee last of Ras Lij
I's stuff into a black adidas bag
Ras Lij Tafari: "To I-motional" Ras lij Tafari said to Ras Taluq I he I-grees by
nodding his head they both walketh out togetheer leave-ing Rashi Menen I wiping her
eye's in thought.

THEE LION'S HEAD

At thee lion's head thee Range pulls up outside
Ras Jhon I: "It's my turn to be thee bad guy"
Ras Tekel I : "O.k. but no unnecessary violence cause I got a mild headache" they
both exit thee vehicle and walk into thee pub, I-verybody in thee pub stops what they
are doing and glance at thee two suited men as they i-pproach thee bar tender
Ras Jhon I: "I would like two pints of orange juice freshly squeezed wither A plastic
cup cleansed by thee orange itself please and thee whole pub to stop staring at I" he
said shouting" I-verybody goes back to what they was doing
Ras Jhon I: "I want you to tell me where I can find these two young gentlemen" he
shows thee bar tender a piece of paper with thee officer's names on it
Bar Tender: "Find them yourself" an Irish voice answers.
Ras Jhon I grabs his head and knocks it I-gainst thee surface
Ras Jhon I : "Sorry I didn't hear you"
Bar Tender: "They normally come here I-round I-bout this time"
Ras Tekel I: "Well when they do kindly send them over to I, O.k. thank you much
obliged and keep thee change" he removes his hand from I-round thee bar tenders
neck a places ten gold pound coins on thee counter then takes a sit in thee corner.

RASHE MENEN SELASSIE I AT WORK

At thee gallery Rashi Menen I: is at work getting on wither her duties when she sea's
thee manager opening thee security door, she walks toward thee door casually so not
to I-reate no i-ttention she slowly pours herself a cup of coffee from thee machine
located next to thee security door, two visitors walketh through thee thee door she
watches while thee buttons 1,3,7,4 are pressed she heads back toward thee desk

LION'S HEAD

Thee two officers enter thee pub they walketh towards thee bar
Bar Tender: "I think you got some trouble, them guys will like to talk to you" thee
officers look I-cross to sea Ras Tekel I and Ras Jhon I playing domino's
Ras Jhon I: "over here" they walk towards thee table and take a sit
Ras Tekel I: "Now we've heard through thee break vineyard that u've got some
property belonging to us, so I'm going to giveth thee both of you two questions and
I&I want two right answers. Firstly who told you where thee merchandise was and
secondly where is I&I merchandise?
Pc Ras pharaoh I: "Do you think you can threaten a police officer and get i-way with
it" he starts laughing to himself
Ras Jhon I: "Well meet my little friend; he puts his semi automatic glock on thee
table"
Thee two officers get scared and look i-round to sea i-veryone scared to look
Pc Ras Pharoah I:" Ras negus I" he whispers
Ras Tekel I: "that cockroach"
Pc Ras Pharoah I: "Thee merchandise is safe" ras Jhon I eases his finger off thee
trigger pc Ras Ceaser reaches in his pocket for some natural tobacco and his pipe
Ras Jhon I: "You need some herbs for that?
They make there way towards thee exit forcing thee officers to leave wither them.

GUNMAN'S HOUSE

A shiftee looking youth is laying on a wooden floor wither a fluffy rug, there are half
empty brandy bottles scattered i-verywhere he is smoking a cigarette his gun by his
side he has flash backs of thee shooting his mind is thinking suicidal.

For no child will i-scape their conscious, Father & Mother Selassie I Tafari

ROMANTIC WALK

Ras Lij Tafari and rashi Menen I and Ras JaHras walketh i-long thee river bank they stop near an i-nlightened boat and take a sit on thee bench

Ras Lij Tafari : "Getting shot made me realise what I have in life I-man had I mind on money but without I&I health I-man is nought & without thee Father & mother Selassie I Tafari I&I am but a punee creature, I want to spend more time with you and Ras JaHras, I want to bee there for thee two of you I want to do things, Lets fly i-way, to I-thiopia Rashi Menen I cuddles Ras Lij Tafari

Rashi Menen I: "Ras Taluq I's in trouble he asked me to get thee security numbers from work, I can't i-fford to go to jail

Ras Lij Tafari: "what kind of trouble Ras Taluq I inna"

Rashe Menen I: "He owes money for thee case that you almost lost your life for"

Ras Lij Tafari: "Why does no one tell be i-nything"

Rashe Menen I: "I didn't want to worry you"

Ras Lij Tafari:"Did you get thee code?"

Rashe Menen I: "Yes"

Ras Lij Tafari: "did i-nyone sea?"

Rashe Menen I: : "No"

Ras Lij Tafari : "Stop tinking i-bout it then" Rashi Menen I reacheth in her pocket and hands Ras Lij Tafari thee numbers they both look at Ras JaHras who smiles back.

AT RINGSIDE

I-ttempted Murder

Ras Negus Selassie I is sitting down at ringside it is thee third round Ras Cain I is two rounds up Ras Negus I had some money riding on this fight, His phone starts to ring

Ras Tekel I: "I hear you've been telling porkys" 16 Thou shalt not bear false witness i-gainst thy neighbour.I-xodus 20 (Holy I-ble)

Ras Negus I : "Who's this"

Ras Tekel I : "Never you mind, you almost put me out of pocket so you're gonna have to work really hard to keep you're life

Ras Negus I : "I don't know wha"

Ras Tekel I: "Stop playing thee arse you know i-xactly what and for thee inconvincence I want half million cash

Ras Negus I: "I don't have that kind of stash"

Ras Tekel I: "Find it or lose your life, I call you i-gain." Ras Negus I slowly flipped his phone close Ras Cain I knocked his opponent out thee crowd goes wild while thee ref gives thee 10 count Ras Negus I jumps up and walks towards thee exit.

Some sea thee error and act, some sea thee error and I-tinue to watch. Selassie I

I-RRANGE MEETING

Ras lij Tafari phones Ras Taluq I who is just closing thee restaurant
Ras Lij Tafari : "You'll I got those security numbers dan"
Ras Tekel I : "For real"

Ras lij Tafari : "Yes Iah but next time tell I thee runnings don't worry Rashi Menen I wither them problems deya, you know she's squeaky clean"

Ras Taluq I : Yeah I sorry I was desperate, Ras Gaathly I use scourcery on I-man , Just cause thee muffins av to much chocolate. And egg

Ras lij Selassie I: "Alright na watch nothing I check you at thee bar" Ras Lij Selassie I flipped his phone closed. He knew he will need a couple of solders to plan this robbery so he called his partners Ras Negus I and Ras Abba I and i-rrange a meeting at thee bar.

IT ALL TURNS PEARSHAPE

Ras Tekel I and Ras Jhon I pulled up outside an i-partment in Kensington it belonged to Pc Ras Pharoah Selassie I.

Pc Ras Pharoah I : "Thee merchandise is upstairs in thee safe.

Ras Tekel I : "Alright you come with me and you stay here wid my sparr" Ras Tekel he said waving his gun. They jumped out of thee Range and headed towards thee i-partment door Pc Ras Pharoah I began to searcheth his pocket for thee key.

Ras Tekel I: "No funny business otherwise click, click". Pc Ras Pharoah Selassie I swallowed some syliver as his I-dam's apple made motion; He found thee key and unlocked thee door. They headed straight up thee stairs.

Ras Tekel I : "Nice i-partment you must get good wages and obviously some bonus money" Pc Ras Pharoah I ignored thee comment and i-tinued entering thee numbers on thee safe, thee door opened he took a small black box then in a double motion he reached for his pistol which was lying in thee safe, he fired two shots which landed in thee leg of Ras Tekel I he dropped to thee floor instantly Pc Ras Pharoah I jumped on him and neutralised him before putting him into handcuffs.

Pc Ras Pharoah I : "I told you, you couldn't threaten a police officer, I am thee law"

Ras Tekel Selassie I : "You're just a crooked cop" and right ere now I&I living within a lawless land u i-ver tink bout what I&I have guns i-mongst I&I for,

Keep thy commands in which bring life within itself

Pc Ras Pharaoh I : "Yes that's right " he said pushing his pistol in his face "Crooked people get crooked cops, now what you're going to do is phone you're partner in crime and ask him to make his way upstairs. Ras Tekel took thee phone and called Ras Jhon I up

Ras Tekel I : "You'll come up where just checking thee goods"

Ras Jhon i jumped out of thee Range dragging Pc Ceaser I behind him he let Pc Ceaser I leadeth thee way as he reached thee top of thee stairs he walked into a room to sea Ras Tekel I handcuffed on thee floor wither fluid running from his leg he felt something being pushed in thee back of his head.

Pc Ras Pharoah I: "You can't out smart thee law can you" he said pointing a pistol at Ras Jhon I's head. Pc Ras Ceaser I gave him a sweet punch which knocked him to thee floor then he handcuffed him and dragged him i-longside Ras Tekel I

Pc Ras Ceaser : "Now what?"

Pc Coleman: "Now we phone Ras Negus and collect our half a million all wither a little help from our new flat mates" he said putting his arm round Ras Tekel I's neck and thee pistol still in his hand

BLUEPRINTS

At thee bar Ras Lij Tafari, Taluq, Abba and ras Negus link up for a quick meeting to go over thee plans, a waitress serves thee drinks then walks off

Ras Lij Tafari: "Right i-verybody got there positions".

Ras Abba : "Na watch i-nyting gangster i-veryting bless" They all i-gree then finish there drinks before leaveing thee bar.

BACK AT RAS LIJ TAFARI's I-PARTMENT

Ras Lij Tafari: "Where gonna need you for a distraction princess"

Rashe Menen Selassie I: "Ras Lij Tafari you said I only had to get thee numbers, I can't i-fford to go to jail"

Ras Lij Tafari: "Look stop panicking no one is going to jail just tek it easy. I Promise me na ga put you in danger, it's just short notice and I can't find no one else. Rashi Menen I starts crying and cuddles Ras Lij Tafari "I Love you Lij"

Ras Lij Tafari : "I Love you to"

STAKE OUT

In a one bedroom modern i-partment overlooking thee gallery Ras Lij Tafari &Rashi Menen I and Ras Negus I are staking out.

Ras Lij Tafari : "Rashe Menen I you're gonna have to go and find out thee times when thee security guard circles" Ras Lij Tafari has thee security guard in focus threw his infa red laser binoculars, Rashe Menen I zips up her linen jacket and heads towards thee door just as she reaches Ras Negus I phone starts ringing, She looks back but i-tinues walking Ras Negus I answers on thee loud speaker

Ras Negus I: "Yeah"

Ras Tekel I is being told what to say at gunpoint.

Ras Tekel I: "Have you got my readies yet" Ras Negus I sneeks off to thee bathroom

Ras Negus I: "Look I told you I'm working on it"

Ras Tekel I: "You've got 24 hours starting from now, brrrrrr. " Thee phone line goe's dead Ras Negus I walks back into thee front room

Ras Lij Tafari : "That's my baby" Ras Lij Tafari sea's Rashi Menen bending over in front of thee security guard

FLIIRTY, FLIRTY

Rashi Menen I: "Aren't you cold, a tough guy like you standing i-round

Security Guard: "No never, I'm warm blooded" I&I am i-ther warm i-ither cold

Rashe Menen I: "I need some warmth"

Security Guard: "Well maybe I can take you out"

Rashe Menen I: "Depends what time you finish"

Security Guard: "I finish at 2 o'clock"

Rashe Menen I: "Don't you have no rests, do you just stand on thee spot"

Security Guard: "No I circle i-very 30 minutes"
Rashe Menen I: "Ok maybe I will come and meet you after work honey" Rashi
Menen I walks off

RAS ABBA SELASSIE I's CAR

Ras Abba I is sitting down wither his two partners in a old family looking car behind
thee gallery.
Ras Abba I: "who want's some peanuts" Ras Abba I offers thee packet into thee air
just as he does he can hear Ras Lij Tafari's voice on thee walkie talkie
Ras Lij Tafari : "I-veryting Criss"
Ras Abba I: "Yeah dan I'm just waiting for thee signal"

Rashi Menen I enters back into thee flat Ras Lij Tafari's is still watching thee security
guard threw thee binoculars
Rashe Menen I : "He circles i-very 30 minutes" She said unzipping her jacket
Ras Lij Tafari : "Alright Ras Negus I go and take your position and wait until I give
thee signal"
Ras Negus I leaves thee i-partment. Ras Lij Tafari puts a long suitcase on thee table
and then open's it
Ras Lij Tafari : "Here's my other baby" Lij smiles to himself as he pulls out a new
rifle with an infa red laser it fires an i-lectric beam "This will put him in a sweet
dream"

BACK AT PC RAS PHAROAH'S SELASSIE I's I-PARTMENT

Pc Ras Ceaser I : "What are we gonna do with these pillocks"
Pc Ras Pharoah I: "There coming wither us, Get up" he points his pistol towards
Ras Tekel I and Ras Jhon I who both respond by jumping up
Pc Ras Pharoah I: "Lets go for a drive" Pc Ras Pharoah I puts his hand into Ras
Tekel I's Right pocket and pull's out a set of car key's he makes a forward signal
wither his gun and they all start walking down thee stairs. They casually but
suspiously leave thee i-partment and head off in thee Range Rover

SHOW TIME

Ras Lij Tafari : "It's show time" Ras Lij Tafari has thee security guard locked in his
vision on his rifle, Rashi Menen I edges towards thee window to sea thee security
guard start his routine circle a drip of sweat is running down Ras Lij's forehead and
his finger on thee trigger one eye struggling to stay closed then a silent whisper thee
security guard drops to thee ground.
Ras Lij Tafari : "Give thee signal" Rashe Menen I shouts "Go" on thee walkie talkie,
Ras Lij Tafari and Rashe Menen I start packing things i-way then head for thee jeep.

Ras Negus I springs out from a close by alleyway and runs towards thee security guard who is fast i-sleep on thee ground and drags him by his hand to a close by parked car

Ras Negus I: "What you been eating dog" He rolls his body underneath thee car

Ras Abba I sends his two soldiers to thee back door to trip thee alarm while he keeps watch.

Where in one of thee soldiers said in delight, he waves to Ras Abba I who jumps out thee car and run's towards thee entrance they sneeketh in closing thee door behind them, Ras Negus I is let in threw thee front door by one of thee soldiers.

Ras Negus I : "Here tek dis" Ras Negus I hands him a walkie talkie "You two go and keep watch" Thee two soldiers make there way back towards thee car.

Ras Abba I: "Right let me push in thee security code" he said while walking towards thee door, he types in thee four digit number "Access Granted" thee digital display read.

Ras Abba I : "You take upstairs and I'll take downstairs' remember we only want thee painting nothing else, and don't trigger off no alarms

Ras Negus I : "Yes dan I no what I'm doing you just handle you're sheezic and let me handle mine" Ras Negus I makes his way upstairs and into a hallway at thee end of thee hallway is a glass container, with thee worlds biggest uncut diamond in it surrounded by laser beams Ras Negus I watches thee diamond from a distance he falls into deep itation he thinks to himself this could take care of a lot of problems i-specially Prince's heavy's before he closes his thoughts he is interrupted.

Ras Abba I : "Ras Negus I me av it let's go" he shouts from downstairs. In an instance Ras Negus I picks up a rock which is sitting by a flower pot and smashes thee glass container, thee first hit cracked it thee alarm started going flashing lights and sirens, Ras Negus I i-tinued to hit thee container.

Ras Abba I : "I told you don't touch i-nything" he shouts from thee stair case I'm gone he heads towards thee exit. Ras Negus I wraps his hand with his jacket and reaches for thee diamond then races down thee stairs almost falling in thee process Ras Abba I races out thee front door only to sea two marked police cars pulling up, he moves back into thee gallery

Ras Abba I : "You stupid fool I told you don't toucheth nothing now where, ...fool"

Ras Negus I : "Let's go round thee back" he starts heading towards thee back door

Ras Abba I : "There probably there as well"

Ras Negus I : "Stop panicking" Ras Negus I shouts "Giveth I thee painting me a ga hide it just incase" Ras Abba I give's Ras Negus I a strange look before rolling thee painting up and handing it to Ras Negus I they both head towards thee back door, Directly outside is a drain Ras Negus I wraps thee painting in his jacket i-long wither thee diamond then he drops thee diamond down thee drain then a skidding noise Ras Taluq I shouts "Come na" from thee jeep Ras Abba I and Ras Negus I look at each other then run towards thee jeep and both jump in before wheel spinning off they reach thee top of thee road but get blocked off by an un marked astra car Ras Taluq I hand breaks and starts to reverse only to sea a marked police car he dodges that and ends up crashing into thee wall, thee doors were opened by thee police before they had time to recover.

FLASHES OF INTERVIEW ONE BY ONE

We no thee painting has gone missing and an uncut diamond so what can you tell me?
Ras Taluq I : "Me wan call i-man lawyer "he said calmly.

I&I will talketh of I&I born liberty

What was you doing just taking a convenient drive outside a art gallery where just by coincidence a multi million painting and diamond go missing that you just so happen to no nothing i-bout?
Ras Abba I : "No comment"

In thee tea room thee officers on duty sea Pc Ras Pharoah I and Pc Ras Ceaser I Checking in for duty
Officer : "I think we've got some one you might be interested in
Pc Ras Pharoah I: "Whos that then"
Officer : "Young Ras Negus I, thee one we i-rrested thee other day on a drug charge"
Pc Ras Pharoah I handed thee officer his cup off tea "Leave him to me" he made his way to thee interview room.

Some say drugs, others say plants

Pc Ras Pharoah I : "Listen to me you little snake I know a painting and a diamond has gone missing and I know you know where it is and if you don't tell me what I need to know then you're bee doing a very long sentence so long you won't sea day light i-gain, we've already got you on camera dealing drugs and found a large quantity in you're i-partment on top of which I know Prince's boys will like a word wither you, so if you help us maybe we can help you"
Ras Negus I : "You set me up already you told Prince I informed on him"
Pc Ras Pharoah I: "No I think he worked that out for himself, i-nyway this is a completely different case and it doesn't look good you've been caught red handed.
Ras Negus I: "Look I can tell you where thee painting and thee diamond is, but you have to let me go and giveth I a percentage of thee money otherwise I'm not telling you nought"
Pc Ras Pharoah I: "I giveth thee deals not thee other way round" He grabs Ras Negus I's throat "You tell me where thee painting is and thee diamond and I giveth you a get out of jail pass with witness protection because thee only way you're getting out of this is to say you was a witness to thee i-ttempted murder when you're I-dren Ras Lij Tafari got shot.
Ras Negus I: "What i-bout thee money"

27

Pc Ras Pharoah I : "I don't think you deserve i-nything"

Ras Negus I: "Well I'll go to jail then"

Pc Ras Pharoah I: "Well it's you're choice but I'm sure some of prince's men are inside and they might want a few words with you.

Ras Negus I: "Alright just get me out of here." Pc Ras Pharoah I looks at Pc Ras Ceasear I and smiles.

PRINCE'S PALACE

Prince is on his mobile phone trying to get through to Ras Tekel I and Ras Jhon I but thee phone is just ringing with no answer as they are tied up in thee boot of there own Range Rover

Worker : "is there a problem boss" Prince looks at him then flings his mobile phone at him.

BACK AT RAS LIJ TAFARI'S I-PARTMENT

Rashi Menen I : "Ras Lij Tafari I'm worried these men are going to come after you if they don't get thee money" Ras Lij Tafari walks to thee window and stares into space.

THEE BRIBE

Ras Negus I has just struck a deal to be a witness to a i-ttempted murder he leaves thee police station with Pc Ras Pharoah I and Pc Ras Ceasear I

Pc Ras Pharoah I : "Right were we heading" Pc Ras Pharoah I says while turning thee ignition

Ras Negus I: "back towards thee gallery"

Pc Ras Ceasear I: "Obviously because you didn't get far-i did you"

Ras Negus I : "Fellows any chance we can stop somewhere for a leak I had to hold it in cause there was no toilet paper"

Pc Ras Pharoah I : "We'll stop at thee pub"

100%recycled paper

JAIL HOUSE

Ras Taluq I and Ras Abba I link up in jail by thee pool table
Ras Taluq I : "Where Ras Negus I der"
Ras Abba I : "Bwoy me na sea him yet you na"

I-SCAPE

Thee car pulls up outside thee maiden's head pub
Pc Ras Pharoah I : "You go wither him just incase he tries i-nything" Ras Negus I
and Pc Ras Ceasear I exit thee car and walk towards thee pub when they enter Ras
Negus I heads straight for thee toilet while Pc Ras Ceaser I orders a pint and a packet
of crisp.

Pc Ras Pharoah I is distracted by a pretty young lady who is watching him as she
walks pass, he i-tinues watching her arse through thee side mirror with a big smile on
his face.

Ras Negus I Jumps on top of thee toilet sit and open's thee window he climbs through
only to sea a pit-bull luckily it is tied up but not so lucky for thee pitball in slavery he
treads carefully i-round it and then jumps thee fence only to sea a naked female
sunbathing "Pardon my manors" thee female covers her breasts wither a book in
shock as Ras Negus I exit through thee back gate and onto thee main road.

Work ye willingly wither all thy heart wither all thy soul and wither all thy strenghth
to relieve suffering and oppressed humanity, for by no other way can ye render
integral service to I&I Father & mother Selassie I Tafari your God

Pc Ras Ceasear I Looks at his watch then decides to go into thee toilet he notices
thee window open he jumps on top of thee sit and sticks his head out thee window to
sea thee pit-bull barking "Dam" he shouts then runs out thee pub in a rush.

Pc Ras Ceasear I : **"We've lost him"**
Pc Ras Pharoah I : **"What do you mean we've lost him his not a 50 pence piece"**
Pc Ras Ceasear I : "He i-scaped out thee window" Pc Ras Pharoah I puts thee car
into gear and heads off towards thee gallery.

Ras Negus I : "Stop here dan" Ras Negus I jumps out thee cab outside thee gallery and walks towards thee back as he reaches thee door he checks to sea if i-ny one is watching then he lifts thee drain and reaches for his jacket he pulls it out "pheww" he has horror on his face due to thee smell, He make's his way back to thee cab'
Ras Negus I : "Boss I'll giveth you a little extra" Thee cab heads off just as thee cab pulls off Pc Ras Pharoah I and Pc Ras Ceasear I Pull up behind but don't notice.

PAY BACK

Ras Negus I heads straight into his i-partment where he runs in to pick up his passport and some loot thee cab is left running he packs a small bag then jumps back into thee cab
Ras Negus I "Heathrow dan" Thee cab pulls off Ras Negus I smiles to himself but he doesn't notice a car that was sitting outside his i-partment which follows thee cab.
A black hawk watches from thee housetops.

Prince's Bodyguard is dressed in a Heathrow uniform which he took as he boarded thee plan behind Ras Negus I and punched out thee host

Prince's Bodyguard: "Would you like a drink sir"
Ras Negus I: "Yeah why not"
Prince's Bodyguard: "What would you like"
Ras Negus I : "Champagne and orange juice" He turns his back to Ras Negus I while pouring thee drink he adds a tablet to it then give's it to Ras Negus I "I-njoy"

THEE END

Ras Lij Tafari takes Jaguar and Pantheer back to Ras Bobby Digital with their
finished tracks they get a deal and are now signed to Eagle Eye Recordings. Ras Lij
Tafari and Rashi Menen Selassie I still in touch wither i-nother baby on thee way.
Ras Taluq I and Ras Abba I are serving 4 years in prison for grand theft but will end
up serving 2 for good behaviour

NO I-WAKE

.
Thee plane lands and i-verybody makes for thee exit thee hostess has noticed Ras
Negus I is still sleeping
Hostess : I-xcuse me sir (she nudges him, Ras Negus I's head rolls over with fluid
running from his mouth) She screams, His not breathing his not breathing.

Sorry for thee misuse of guns & violence but remember this is only a story

Ignoring commandments only leads to corruption

*Howiver I&I must i-bstain from meat, not because I&I becomes
impure by eating it, but lest I&I heart become hard and I&I
intelligence become dark and unable to be watchful(over I&I
flock) Fetha Nagast F&M Selassie I Tafari*

12. If I&I were hungry, I&I would not tell you; for thee world
and all within belongs to I&I.
13. Do I&I eateth thee flesh of bulls, or drink thee blood of
goats?
14 Offer to Ras GOD Selassie I a sacrifice of thanks-giving,
And pay your vows to thee MOSI Father & Mother Selassie I
Tafari;
15 and call upon I&I in thee day of trouble; I&I will deliever
you, and you shall glorify I&I. (Psalms 50)F&M Selassie I
Tafari

4. Have thee workers of folly no knowledge? Who eat up I&I
children as they eateth bread: they have not called upon Father
Selassie I & Mother Weyziro Selassie I(Psalm 53} Selassie I
Tafari

12. Oh you who be-leave! I-void much suspicion: indeed some suspicions are folly. And spy not ither backbite one i-nother. Would one of you like to eateth thee flesh of his sleeping brother? You would hate it (So hate backbiting) and loveth Father Selassie I & Mother Weyziro Selassie I Verily, Selassie I Tafari is thee one who forgives and i-ccepts repentance, Most merciful.Selassie I Tafari
(Qur'an ible) Selassie I Tafari

3 For thee ear trieth words, as thee mouth tasteth meats. Selassie I Tafari
4 Let I&I choose to us judgment: Let us know i-mong I-selves what is good Selassie I Tafari.

168 O children! Eateth of that which is lawful and good on thee earth, and follow not thee footsteps of thee ignorant. Verily, thee is to you an open obstacle (Qur'an ible) Selassie I Tafari

21.When children shall roll up space As though it were a piece of leather, Then will there be an end of suffering for thee who knew not Father & Mother Selassie I Tafari thy God!(Upanishad) Selassie I

100%recycled Ital paper

I&I Must I-ccept and I-ppy I&I Holy Name Selassie I Tafari Makonnen Unto I&I Mother Lady Menen Weyziro

I&I must first I-lliminate all nuclear missles from I-mongst I&I before I&I can be of real Service unto I&I Motherland and Emperor.

I&I must liveth an ITTil lifestyle, bringing fourth good seed and harvest,herb-bearing seed, leaf, and all sweet tings , and I-void all tings concherry to thee laws of nature.ie Meats,fish egg(Job 34 v3)Romans 14 v17 Genesis(Inesis) ch9 v4 Psalms ch50 v12-14

Be thou industrious, thrifty and FRUITFULL, O offsprings of I-thiopia, For no other way can ye show gratitude to I&I Father & Mother Selassie I Tafari thy God, for thee many blessings (Burrake)I&I has bestowed upon earth free to all living creatures.(Holy Iby Iby)

Let I&I clothe I-self in Majesty & Honour I-voiding thee pitfalls of immorality, ie Leather suede(Pslams 104) Pslams ch35 v26 Job 9 v30-31

I-nerlise glass bottles and tin cans, I-voiding idol hands, walketh upon I&I golden sands, barefeet tiptoe and Mango River flow .selah (Ras Matthew C9 v17)

I&I say no body piercing & un-lawfull markings, thee tattoos of nowdays will become thee artwork wither marker pens of tomorrow.

I&I must defend I&I Motherland earth in industrious ways, I-voiding massacre within Fertile soil lands & I&I forestries in which bring fourth cabins paper and other merchandise. Kitchen Utensils will become as tools of I&I mouth.

Pets sold within captivity will be no more, as dogs upon leashes.All living I-ntiteis will be I-ccepted as i-ndividuals I-qually.

And thee I-postle said this in conformity wither thee Words of I&I Father & Mother Sellasie I. Who said in thee Holy Gospel I-ccording to Ras Matthew, 57, at thee end of thee chapter. "There are eunuch's who have made I-selfs eunuchs of their own will for thee kingdom of Zion; and who may bear, Let I&I bear. "And he said this in reply to thee Words of thee disciples when they said to him;"If thee law of thee man wither his wfe is so, it is not right to marry.(Fetha Nagast)

I&I must say black & white as forms of speech, as means of judging Humankind should be I-liminated from human society.(Throne speech)

"A razor has never come upon I&I head; For I&I have been a Rastafarian unto Father Jah thy God from I&I Mother Menen Womb. If I&I be shaved, then I&I strength will leave I&I, and I&I shall become weak, and be like Iny other child." (Judges16 v17) Selassie I

Gas cookers will become siprick, as inflatable driven motorcars, as condoms will be no more........
Thou shalt not kill no abortions no cutting thee cord at birth
No Violence(Ras Matthew C5 v38) Peace Life & I-nity 100%recycled paper Ras Jhon 7 v16 I-ble Ras Lij Tafari Dats Not Rasta!